Four Good Friends

Modern Curriculum Press
BEGINNING
TO
READ
Series

Four Good Friends

Margaret Hillert
Illustrated by Krystyna Stasiak

ISBN: 0-8136-5561-7
Printed in the United States of America

18 19 20 21 22 23 24   06 05 04 03 02

Modern
Curriculum
Press

Pearson Learning Group

1-800-321-3106
www.pearsonlearning.com

I can not work.
No one wants me.
I have to go away.
Away, away, away.

5

Oh, my. Oh, my.
You do not look good, little one.
Why?
What is it?

I can not work.
No one wants me.
I am no good.

Come. Come.
I like you.
You can come with me.

See here now.
We will go away.
We will find something.

9

What is this?
What have we here?
You are a big one.

I can not run.
I can not work.
What will I do now?
Where will I go?

You are big.
Big, big, big.
You can help us.

You can come with us.
We want you.
Come with us to see
what we can find.

My, how pretty you are.
But, what is it?
Can we help?

I am no good, I guess.
No one wants me.
What am I to do?

15

Do you want to come with us?
We like you.
We want you.

Look here.
A little house.
Is this what we want?

Have a look.

What do you see?

What is in this house?

19

20

I see a man.
I see two.
I see three.

We want to see, too.
Do it like this.
Here we go.
Up and up and up.

24

Oh, oh, oh!
Oh, my. Oh, my!
Oh, look at that!

Get out! Get out!
It is not good for us here.
Get away! Get away!
Run, run, run.

Now that is funny.
What did we do?
But come in here.
It looks good in here.

29

Now we have a house.
We have something to eat.
We do not have to work.
We are happy.

31

Margaret Hillert, author of several books in the MCP Beginning-To-Read Series, is a writer, poet, and teacher.

Four Good Friends uses the 61 words listed below.

a	get	man	that
am	go	me	this
and	good	my	three
away	guess		to
		no	too
big	happy	not	two
but	have	now	
	help		up
can	here	oh	us
come	house	one	
	how	out	want(s)
did			we
do	I	pretty	what
	in		where
eat	is	run	why
	it		will
find		see	with
for	like	something	work
funny	little		
	look(s)		you